The New
Open Highways

More Power

Authors Ida Mae Johnson
Alfonso R. Ramirez
Mildred Beatty Smith
John C. Manning
Joseph M. Wepman
Lorraine M. Sullivan
William A. Jenkins
Ira E. Aaron
Helen M. Robinson
A. Sterl Artley
Marion Monroe

Andrew Schiller Linguistics Advisor

Editorial Direction: Erma Stewart
Development: Joy Ingersoll
Design and Graphics: Catherine Koehler and
James L. Ballard with Wendy Wallen and Marcy Levine

ISBN: 0-673-04705-9

Regional offices of Scott, Foresman and Company are
located in Dallas, Texas; Glenview, Illinois; Oakland,
New Jersey; Palo Alto, California; Tucker, Georgia;
and Brighton, England.

Contents

SECTION ONE

SECTION TWO

SECTION THREE

SECTION FOUR

Section I

Michael's Real Live Animals

Michael liked animals.
He read books about animals.
He liked the books a lot, but he wanted
to see some real, live animals.

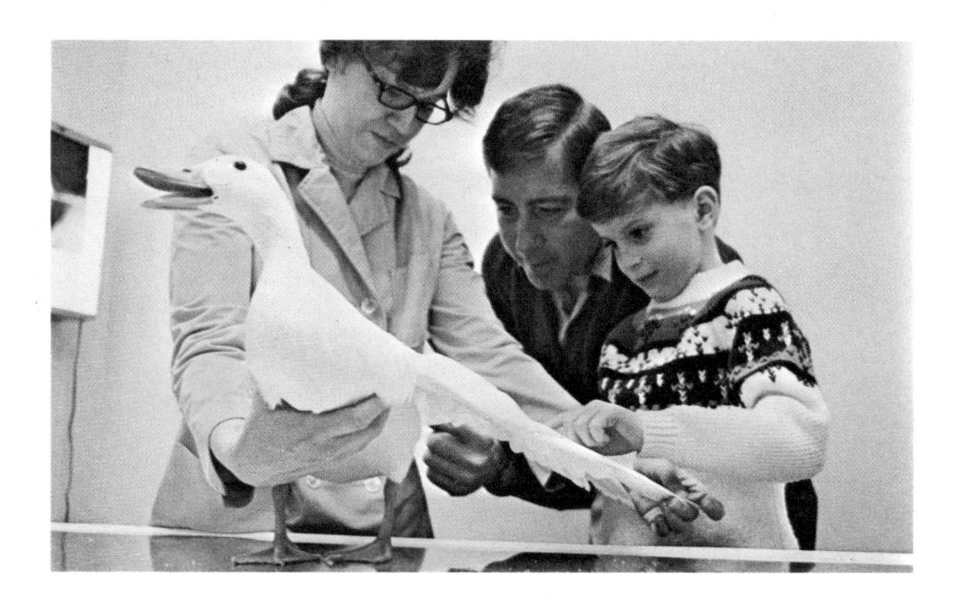

Michael's dad took him to visit a veterinarian.
Michael touched a duck's feathers.

He listened to a dog's heart.

Then Michael and his dad went to an aquarium.
A diver was under the water feeding some fish.

Later Michael and
his dad went to
a zoo.
They saw the
meat that
tigers eat.

The tiger liked
its dinner.

When it was time to go home, Michael said good-by to a chimpanzee.

Michael liked the real, live animals a lot.

How to Care for a Goldfish

Get a big bowl with a big opening at the top.
Put water in the bowl.
Let the water stand two or three days.

Put a water plant in
the bowl.
Place the bowl where
the plant will get
a little sunlight
each day.

Get a small
goldfish from a
pet store.
Put the fish into
the bowl.
Do not touch the
goldfish with your
hands.

Feed your goldfish one *small* pinch of fish food each day.

Change the water in the fish bowl every three days.
Always use water that has stood two or three days.

When You Read

Pictures can
help you when
you read.

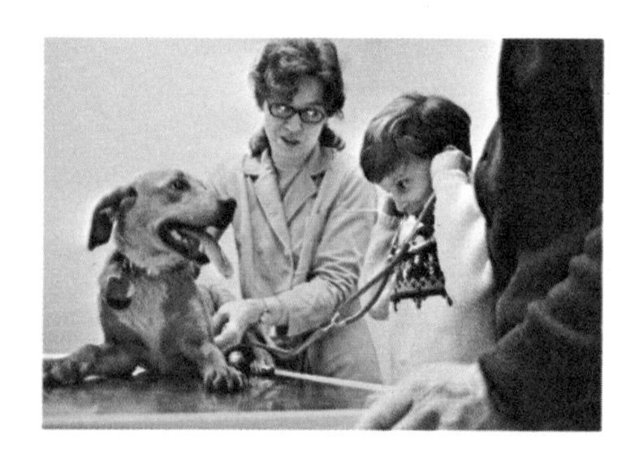

These pictures
helped you
read **dog**
and **tiger.**

Consonant
letters can
help you, too.

Consonant letters helped you read the last word in this sentence.

The tiger liked its d-nn-r.

Consonant letters and the way words are put together helped you read this sentence.

He l-st-n-d to the dog's h--rt.

Using the Pictionary

man
king
wax paper
candy
goldfish
city
spatula
giant
country

Pogo Leaves the Circus

Pogo was a clown in a circus.
Every day he rode an elephant.
The elephant's name was Mabel.
Pogo and Mabel were very good friends.

At last Pogo got too old to be a clown.
So he had to leave the circus.
He was very sad.
He did not want to leave Mabel.

Pogo thought, "Maybe I can buy Mabel.
Then we'll both be happy.
I'll go ask the man who runs the circus."

"Hello, Mr. James," said Pogo.
"I have to leave the circus.
But I don't want to leave Mabel.
We've been friends for a long time.
Could I buy Mabel and take her with me?"

Mr. James said, "I'm sorry, Pogo.
I can't sell her to you."

Pogo was very, very sad.

That night Pogo went to the elephant tent.
He went to say good-by to Mabel.

All at once the lights in the tent came on.
There were all of Pogo's circus friends.
"Surprise! Surprise!" they cried.

And there was Mabel with a big sign that said TO POGO.

Mr. James said, "This is why I couldn't
sell Mabel to you, Pogo.
Your friends bought her for you.
They bought her as a surprise."

"Oh my!" said Pogo.
"What a fine surprise!"

A clown yelled, "You'd better save
every cent you can, Pogo.
You'll need it to feed Mabel."

Everyone laughed, and Mabel winked one
little eye.

Holding Hands

by Lenore M. Link

Elephants walking
Along the trails
Are holding hands
By holding tails.

Trunks and tails
Are handy things
When elephants walk
In circus rings.

"Holding Hands" by Lenore M. Link from *St. Nicholas*, Vol. 63, No. 8 (June 1936).

Elephants work
And elephants play
And elephants walk
And feel so gay.

And when they walk—
It never fails
They're holding hands
By holding tails.

Laugh Time

Did you know peanuts will make you fat?
How do you know?
Did you ever see a skinny elephant?

Pennies for Ziggy

This is Ziggy the elephant.
He came to Brookfield Zoo many years ago.
Soon Ziggy and his keeper were good friends.

Ziggy had been around people most of his life.
But he was still a wild elephant.
Some days Ziggy became very dangerous.
Even his keeper was not safe with him.

The people at the zoo worried that Ziggy would hurt someone.
So for years Ziggy had to live inside the elephant house.
He could not go outside like the other elephants did.
The people at the zoo wanted Ziggy to be able to go outside.
So they asked for money to build a new home for Ziggy.

People all over the world sent money.
Many children gave their pennies for Ziggy.

Ziggy's stall in the elephant house was
fixed up.
A yard was built for Ziggy outside his stall.

Then one day Ziggy came outside for
the first time in years!

From his yard Ziggy can make friends with the other zoo elephants.

Visitors can see him enjoying the new home they made possible.

The Giant's Hiccups

Once upon a time a friendly giant lived
in a little town.
The people in the town liked the giant.
And the giant liked having so many friends.

But one day the giant
got the hiccups.
"HIC, HIC," said the giant
all day long.
The giant's hiccups
were so loud that
the people couldn't work.

"HIC, HIC," said the giant
all night long.
The giant's hiccups
were so loud that
the people couldn't sleep.

"HIC, HIC, HIC," said the giant.
"HIC, HIC, HIC."

The people didn't know what to do.
"How can we stop the giant's hiccups?"
they asked.

"We could scare him," someone said.

"How could *we* scare a *giant?*" asked
another person.

"We couldn't," said the people.
No one knew what to do.

Some people said, "We could ask the giant to leave town."

A little girl heard the people talking.
She didn't want the giant to leave.
"I will help him," said the little girl.

The little girl walked up the giant's foot.

"HIC, HIC, HIC," said the giant.

She walked up the giant's arm.

"HIC, HIC, HIC," said the giant.

The little girl stood on the giant's shoulder.
She yelled to the giant, "Giant, hold your breath and count to twenty."

"HIC," said the giant.
He held his breath and started to count.

All the people in the town waited.
No one made a sound.

Then all that the people could hear were the birds singing.
It was quiet all over the town.
The giant didn't have the hiccups anymore.

Section 2

Junk Day on Juniper Street

based on a story idea by Lilian Moore

One day Davy and his parents were reading the newspaper.

Davy's mother said, "Look at this!"

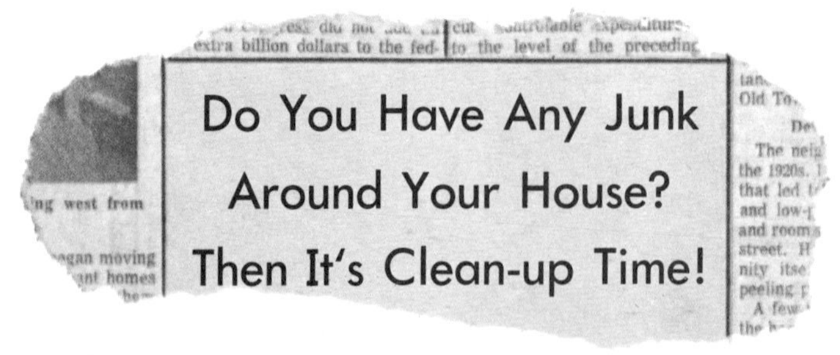

Do You Have Any Junk
Around Your House?
Then It's Clean-up Time!

Later Davy's mother saw Beth and
Beth's mother going by.

Davy's mother asked, "Did you see
the newspaper this morning?
It said we should have a clean-up time."

"Well, why not?" said Beth's mother.

Davy's mother asked some of her friends
to come over.

They said, "We all have junk.
Lots and lots and lots of junk!
Let's clean up!
Let's have a Junk Day on Juniper Street!"

So Juniper Street had a Junk Day.
It was a big clean-up time.

Soon there was junk outside of
every house.
There were old tables, chairs, and toys.
There were all kinds of things.

Davy's mother called a junkman.
She said, "Bring a big truck to
Juniper Street tomorrow.
You'll need it to pick up all the junk."

People walked by the piles of junk.

Davy said, "There's a good wheel.
I can fix my wagon with it."

Beth's father saw a toolbox.
He said, "I can fix that toolbox.
It will be as good as new."

Many people found things they liked.

Davy's mother found a table.
She said, "That table would look new
with some red paint."

Beth's mother said, "I can use this
hatbox. I need a box to store things in."

The next morning the junkman came.
All the junk on Juniper Street was gone but one big chair.

"Well, well!" said the junkman.
"This is just what I've been looking for."

He put the chair in the truck.
And off he went with the junk from Juniper Street.

When You Read

Each compound word is made up of two root words.

A newspaper is a ____ with ____ in it.
A junkman is a ____ who takes ____ away.
A toolbox is a ____ to keep ____ in.
Afternoon is the part of the day right ____ ____.

Some of the following words are root words with the ending -s or -es added.

 lamp

 toolbox

 pants

 lamps

 toolboxes

 pants

 cage

 bus

 woman

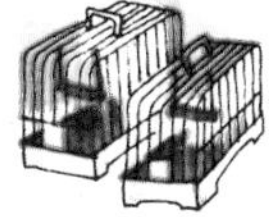 cages

 buses

 women

When You Read

Each underlined word below is a root word with the ending -s, -ed, or -ing added.

Davy looks out the window.
Davy looked out the window.
Davy is looking out the window.

Davy's mother calls a junkman.
Davy's mother called a junkman.
Davy's mother is calling a junkman.

Each underlined word below is a root word with the ending -<u>es</u>, -<u>ed</u>, or -<u>ing</u> added.

Davy <u>watches</u> the people.
Davy <u>watched</u> the people.
Davy is <u>watching</u> the people.

Beth's father sees a toolbox.
Beth's father saw a toolbox.
Beth's father is <u>seeing</u> a toolbox.

Someday, Sara

One day Sara went to the airport with
her parents.
They liked to watch the planes.

"I'd like to ride in an airplane,"
Sara said.

"Someday, Sara," said her mother.

"I'd even like to fly an airplane,"
Sara said.

"Someday, Sara," said her mother.

"Maybe I'll go to the moon in a rocket,"
Sara said.

"Someday, Sara," said her mother.

There were lots of things Sara wanted to do.
She decided to make a book about them.
Sara called it *My Someday Book.*

She drew a picture of
herself flying a plane.

She drew a picture of
herself on the moon.

Sara drew lots of other pictures.
Then she put them in her book.

Then one day some builders came to build
a house next door to Sara's.
Every day Sara watched them work.

One afternoon she told her mother,
"I'm going to build a house too."

"Someday, Sara," said her mother.

"No," said Sara.
"I'm going to build it now."

"Well, how are you going to do that?"
asked her mother.

"You'll see," said Sara.
"I'll need a hammer and saw and some nails.
I'll ask the builders for some boards they
aren't going to use."

Sara got the boards.
Then her mother showed her how to use
the hammer and the saw.

Sara took the things into the backyard.
She worked all afternoon.

At dinner Sara told her father about
the house she built.

He said, "When you grow up maybe you
can build a real house."

"This *is* a real house," said Sara.
"Come to the backyard, and I'll show you."

Sara and her parents went to the backyard. There was Sara's house, hanging from a tree.

"It's a real house, Sara," said her mother.

"It's a real birdhouse," said her father.

A Gift You Can Make

You will need:

a pencil

a spool

a tube of glue

paint

First paint your spool.

Next put some glue on the pencil below the eraser band.

Last, slip the spool over the eraser onto the glue.

Hard-Hat Jobs

Some people have dangerous jobs.
Many of them wear hard hats.
The hard hats protect their heads.

These men work in a steel mill.

This man is making a hole in the street.
He is using a jackhammer.

A subway will be built under the street.
A subway is a railroad that travels
under the streets.

This man works in a coal mine.
He wears a mask.
The mask keeps out the dust.

Can you guess why he has a light
on his hat?

This woman is an architect.
She plans new buildings.
Her plans for a big building are on the
blue papers.
She is talking with a builder about the plans.

These firemen put out fires in city buildings.

Can you think of other jobs where people wear hard hats?

Jimmy's Pocket-Aunt

"Jimmy," said Grandma Jones.
"I'm busy this morning.
You take care of your Aunt Alice."

Aunt Alice was only three years old.
Jimmy was five years older than
Aunt Alice.
He did not like to take care of her.
All his friends laughed at him.
They thought it was funny to have
such a little aunt.

Jimmy took Aunt Alice out into the yard.
He began to read, and Aunt Alice played.

Soon Jimmy heard music coming from
the park.
But he did not hear Aunt Alice.
He jumped up and looked around.
No Aunt Alice!

Jimmy ran to the park to look for her.
He could not find her anywhere.

A policeman named Mr. Lee came along.
"What's your name?" asked Mr. Lee.
"And what's the trouble?"

Jimmy said, "My name is Jimmy Jones.
My Aunt Alice is lost."

"What does she look like?" said Mr. Lee.
"Is she young or old?"

Jimmy told Mr. Lee what she looked like.
But he did not want the policeman to know
that she was only three.
So Jimmy said, "I guess you could say
that Aunt Alice is young."

The policeman and Jimmy went into
the park building.
"Will Jimmy Jones's Aunt Alice come to
the park building?" called the policeman.

Mr. Lee called four times.
But Jimmy knew Aunt Alice could not
find the park building.

Mr. Lee said, "Just sit there, Jimmy.
Lost boys are always found in this park."

"I'm not lost!" Jimmy said.
"My Aunt Alice is lost."

Jimmy thought, "Maybe I should tell
him Aunt Alice is only three years old."

Just then a policeman walked in.
He said, "Here's another lost child."

"That's my Aunt Alice!" said Jimmy.

Mr. Lee said, "What a pretty little aunt!
I had a little aunt when I was a boy.
I called her my pocket-aunt.
I liked her.
All the other boys wanted a pocket-aunt
like mine."

Jimmy thanked the two men.
Then he started off to his grandmother's house with Aunt Alice.

Jimmy said to himself, "Mr. Lee liked his little aunt.
I like mine, too.
Who said aunts have to be big?
No one!
I'm glad I have a pocket-aunt!"

Using a Map

How did Jimmy go to get to the park building?
How did he go to get home?

Section 3

Candy for Dinner

Tim gave the ball to Mickey.
"I have to go home now," Tim said.
"Dad is bringing Candy for dinner."

Mickey thought, "Candy for dinner!
I wonder what kind it will be."

Tim started to hurry home.
Mickey called to Tim, "May I come
for dinner?
I won't eat much!"

"Sure!" Tim said. "Ask your mom!"
So Mickey hurried home, too.

"Mom!" Mickey called from the door.
"May I eat dinner at Tim's house?"

Mother said, "Did Mrs. Blake ask you?"

Ring! Ring! Ring!
Mickey answered the telephone.

"Mom!" he said.
"Mrs. Blake said I could come."

"All right," said his mother.

Mickey thought about
big bags of candy
while he dressed.

He thought about
round boxes of candy
when he ran out
of the house.

He thought about deep
dishes of candy on the
way down the street.

He thought about
tall jars of candy
as he knocked
on Tim's door.

Tim opened the door.
The two boys went into the dining room.

"Hello, Mickey," said Mr. Blake.
"Candice, I want you to meet Mickey.
Mickey, this is Tim's cousin, Candice."

Candice and Mickey said hello.
Then they all began to eat.
Mickey tried not to eat too fast.
But he kept thinking about the candy.

At last it was time for dessert.
Mrs. Blake came in with a big apple pie.

"How good that looks!" Mickey thought.
"I wonder why they're having apple pie
and candy for dessert.
Well, two desserts are better than one."

Mrs. Blake said, "Mickey, I thought
you and Candy would like this dessert."

Mickey began to laugh.
He said, "The joke's on me!
I thought Mr. Blake was bringing candy
home for dessert.
I didn't know Candy was a girl's name."

Everyone laughed.
Mrs. Blake said, "Come again, Mickey.
Then we'll have both Candy and
candy dessert!"

Peanut Butter Creams

You will need:

a large mixing bowl
a mixing spoon
a measuring cup

a spatula or knife
wax paper

I /4 cup confectioners' sugar
I cup chocolate chips

I /2 cup sweetened
condensed milk
I cup peanut butter

How to make the creams:

1. Put the confectioners' sugar in the bowl.

2. Add the chocolate chips.

3. Add the milk.

4. Add the peanut butter.

5. Stir everything together with the spoon.

6. Drop pieces of candy onto the wax paper.

7. Chill the candy.

8. Eat the candy.

Peanuts

This is a field of
peanut plants.
You can't see the
peanuts because
they grow under
the ground.

This is a drawing
of a peanut plant.
Find the part of
the plant that
grows under the
ground.
Do you see the
peanuts?

When the peanuts
are ripe, a machine
is used to pull up
the plants.

At a factory a machine roasts the peanuts.
Another machine grinds the peanuts to turn them into peanut butter.
The peanut butter is put into cans and jars to be sold.

When You Read

pan	shape	play	hard
bag	gave	stayed	arm
pass	ate		barn
act	rake	paint	sharp
asked	hates	raining	started

not was　　not have　　not said

10
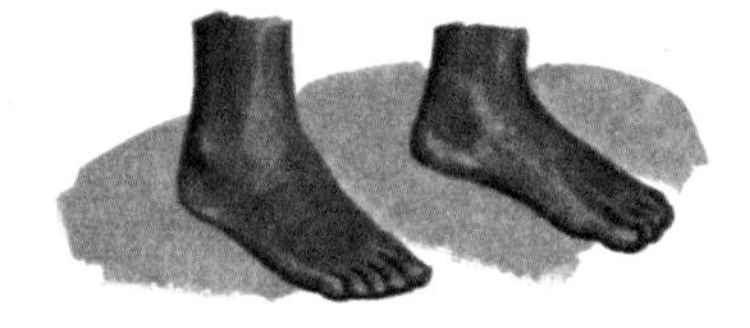

best	wheel	sleeve	fern
fell	peeped	sneezed	her
desk			stern
left	eat	please	clerk
elf	lean	leaves	herd
kept	sea		term
selling	reaches	these	jerked

not few　　not dead

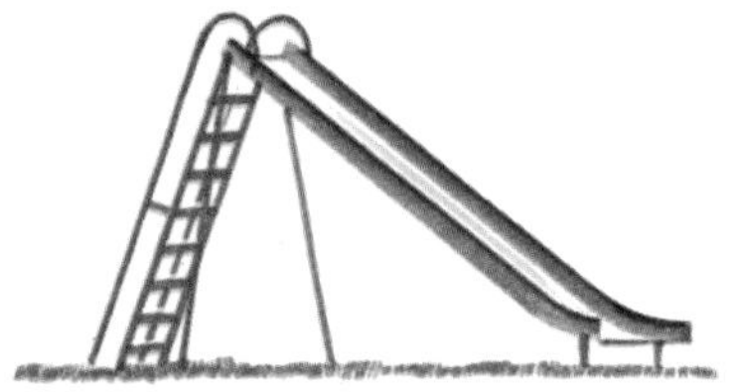
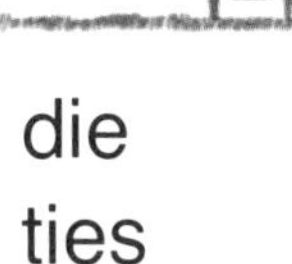

sniff	nice	die	stir
mixing	likes	ties	chirped

not kind　　not give　　not friend

dot	those	hoe	north
drop	broke		or
shot	drove	road	born
locked	noses	boating	porches

not lost　　not one　　not board　　not work

shut	cute	blue	curb
puffing	used	glued	turning

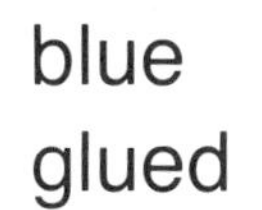

Billy's Find

Mother put ten bags of doughnuts in
Billy's basket.
"There's one bag for every house in
this block," she said.

Billy said, "Mrs. Day won't take one.
She told me not to come by again."

"Then stay away," said Mother.

Billy left with the doughnuts.

Billy went along the block selling
his doughnuts.
Soon he came to Mrs. King's house.

Billy thought, "I hope Mrs. King will buy
the last two bags.
I know Mrs. Day won't buy any doughnuts.
And her house is the only one left."

But Mrs. King needed only one bag.
So Billy still had one bag of doughnuts.

Billy started home.
Just then he heard an animal cry.
The cry came from a box outside
Mrs. Day's fence.

Billy saw a puppy in the box.
He picked it up and petted it.
"You look hungry," said Billy.
"Here's a doughnut, puppy.
I'll take you home and give you some milk."

Then Billy saw Mrs. Day looking out of
her window.

He thought, "Mrs. Day might like
this puppy.
She is all alone.
Oh! She wouldn't want him."

Billy started home again.
Then he walked back and rang
Mrs. Day's bell.

Mrs. Day opened the door.
Billy said, "I'm not selling doughnuts.
I thought you might like this little puppy.
I found him in a box by your fence."

Mrs. Day took the puppy in her arms.
She asked, "Are you sure you found him?"

"Oh, yes!" answered Billy.

Mrs. Day said, "Well, I'll keep him if
you don't want him."

Mrs. Day looked in Billy's basket.
"I'll buy that bag of doughnuts," she said.

"The bag isn't full," said Billy.
"I gave the puppy one."

"That's all right," said Mrs. Day.
"It's my dog, so I'll pay for a full bag.
And I'll buy a bag every week."

She paid Billy, and he started home.
He thought, "Mrs. Day looks happy now.
And I sold all my doughnuts.
Yippee!"

My Puppy

by Aileen Fisher

It's funny
my puppy
knows just how I feel.

When I'm happy
he's yappy
and squirms like an eel.

When I'm grumpy
he's slumpy
and stays at my heel.

It's funny
my puppy
knows such a great deal.

"My Puppy" from *Up the Windy Hill* by Aileen Fisher. Published by Scott, Foresman and Company.

Section 4

Sylvester

Sylvester was a little mouse.
He lived in the country because he
loved music.
He loved to hear the songs of the birds.
He loved to hear the wind in the trees.

One day some people came to build a road.
They dug up Sylvester's home in
the country.
So he went to find a new home in the city.

Sylvester looked and looked for a home.
One day he heard music.
The music came from a music store.
Sylvester went in.
The first thing he saw was a guitar.

Sylvester thought, "This will be a fine house for me.
It has a wire fence in front of the door.
I'll go inside my little house right now!"

Sylvester liked his new house.
He liked going in and out of his door.
He made music when he ran across
the wire fence.
Plink! Plink! Plonk! Plonk!

Every night Sylvester made music on
the wire fence.
People going by the store could hear him.
Plink! Plink! Plonk! Plonk!

People told the storekeeper about the music they heard at night.
One night the storekeeper stayed in the store.

Sylvester began to play. Plunk! Plunk!
The storekeeper heard the music.
He did not see Sylvester in the dark.

"This is magic!" said the storekeeper.
"A magic guitar that plays by itself!"

Many people heard about the magic guitar.
A man named Tex heard about it.
He lived way out West.

Tex loved music, and he loved to sing.
But he could not play a guitar.

Tex went to the city.
He found the magic guitar and bought it.
Sylvester was inside sleeping.

Tex started back to the West.
He stopped to rest when it got dark.
All at once Tex heard music.
He sat up and saw Sylvester.

"I don't have a magic guitar!" said Tex.
"I have a magic mouse!"

Tex and Sylvester became good friends.
Sylvester played the guitar, and Tex sang.
They went here. They went there.
And everywhere they went, they made music together.

Oh, Susanna!

by Stephen Foster

It rained all night the day I left,
the weather it was dry, the
sun so hot I froze to death,
Susanna, don't you cry.

Oh, Susanna! Oh,
don't you cry for me, for I
come from Alabama with my
banjo on my knee.

But Then

by Aileen Fisher

A tooth fell out
and left a space
so big my tongue
can touch my FACE.

And every time
I smile, I show
a space where something
used to grow.

I miss my tooth,
as you may guess,
but then—I have to
brush one less!

"But Then" from *Up the Windy Hill* by Aileen Fisher.
Published by Scott, Foresman and Company.

Excitement on Appleby Street

Joey walked down Appleby Street.
He thought about his tooth.
It was about to come out.

Joey wanted it to come out so he could wish on it.
He wanted to wish for some goldfish.

Just then Joey saw an open manhole.
There was a fence around the hole.
Red flags and a sign were on the fence.
The sign said MEN WORKING.

Joey looked into the manhole.
Then he sneezed.
His tooth fell out of his mouth.
It fell down into the manhole.

"My tooth!" cried Joey.
"I lost my tooth down there!"

All at once some men inside the manhole started yelling.
"I'll get it," yelled one man.

"Call the police!" cried another man.

Then a man came out of the manhole.
He ran down the street.

"It's just a tooth!" called Joey.
But no one heard him.

People came running from all over.
A big fire truck came around the corner.

Then another truck pulled up.
Men jumped off it with picks and shovels.

Joey did not think about his tooth.
All he thought about was the excitement
on Appleby Street.

A road-breaker came next.
It stopped a few feet from the manhole.
It started to make a hole in the street.

"The water pipe broke!" called a man.
"Turn off the water!"

Some other men climbed down into
the manhole.
And at last the water stopped.

Joey thought, "This excitement was fun.
But I'll go home now.
I guess the men will bring my tooth to my house later."

Joey went home.
He told his father about his tooth and about all the men looking for it.

"Oh, Joey!" laughed Father.
"The water pipe broke under
Appleby Street.
The men were running to help fix it.
I don't think they were looking for
your tooth."

The men won't find it!" cried Joey.
"And I won't get my wish!
I won't get my goldfish."

Father said, "Sometimes a tooth under
the street works fine.
Sometimes it works better than a tooth
under the pillow!"

So that night in bed Joey
went on wishing for
his goldfish.

Morning came.
Joey woke up and looked around
his room.
Yes, the goldfish were there!
Three tiny goldfish in a big bowl!

"Dad was right," thought Joey.
"A tooth under the street works just as
well as a tooth under the pillow.
My goldfish will be as much fun as
all the excitement on Appleby Street."

Zachary for Z

Zachary was new in the neighborhood.
He was on his way to his new school.
But he did not want to go to school.

"Oh my," thought Zachary.
"I hope no one laughs at my name.
I wish I had a name like Tom, Bill, or Joe!
I'd like any name but Zachary!"

Zachary got to school early.
Many children were playing in the schoolyard.
But Zachary did not want to play with them.

Zachary crossed the street and sat down on a park bench.
He waited for the bell to ring.
He thought, "Will the kids at this school call me Zachary-Quackery?
The kids at the last school did."

Just then an old man sat down on the bench beside Zachary.
"Hello, I'm Mr. Sutton," said the man.
"What's your name?
I haven't seen you before."

Zachary looked down at his shoes.
He wanted to say that his name was Tom, Bill, or Joe.
But he said, "I'm new here.
My name is Zachary Jones."

Mr. Sutton smiled.
"Zachary!" he said.
"What grade are you in?"

"Second," answered Zachary.

Mr. Sutton said, "Well! Well!
My daughter teaches second grade.
Her class has been waiting for
a Zachary!"

"That's funny!" Zachary said.
"Most kids laugh at my name."

"These children won't!" said Mr. Sutton.
"There's the bell.
Come on!
I'll take you to your room.
I want to see the children's faces when
they hear your name."

Mr. Sutton and Zachary went to the classroom.
The children were in their seats.
Miss Sutton was writing on the board.

Mr. Sutton said, "You have a new pupil this morning, Miss Sutton."

"Hello there," said Miss Sutton. "What's your name?"

"Zachary Jones," answered Zachary.

"Does Zachary begin with a Z?" asked a girl.

"Yes, it does," answered Zachary.

The children began to clap.
"Zachary for Z!" they said.
"Now we have all of our alphabet!"

Zachary looked surprised.

Miss Sutton said, "We have twenty-five children in this room.
Each child's name begins with a different letter of the alphabet.
We were missing one letter.
We were missing the letter Z.
We are lucky you came to our room!"

Zachary was happy.
He thought, "I'm glad my name isn't Tom, Bill, or Joe.
I'm glad I'm Zachary for Z!"

Pictionary

People

boy girl twins

child children

People

man men

woman women

fireman

policeman

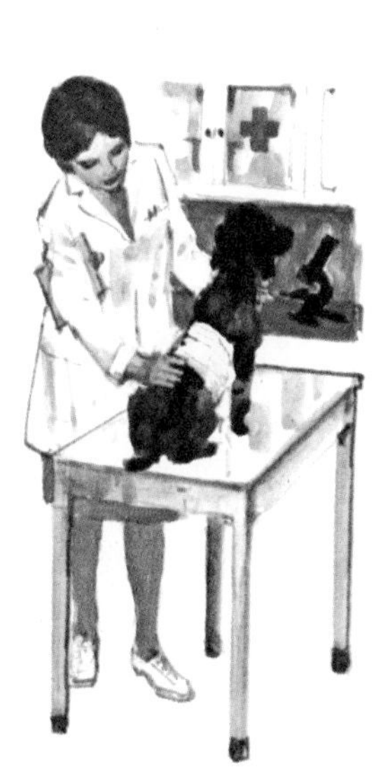

veterinarian

Animals

dog

puppy

cat

kitten

Animals

eel

goldfish

tiger

chimpanzee

crow

Storybook Characters

king

queen

princess

dragon

Storybook Characters

fairy

wizard

clown

giant

Things

airplane

truck

fire truck

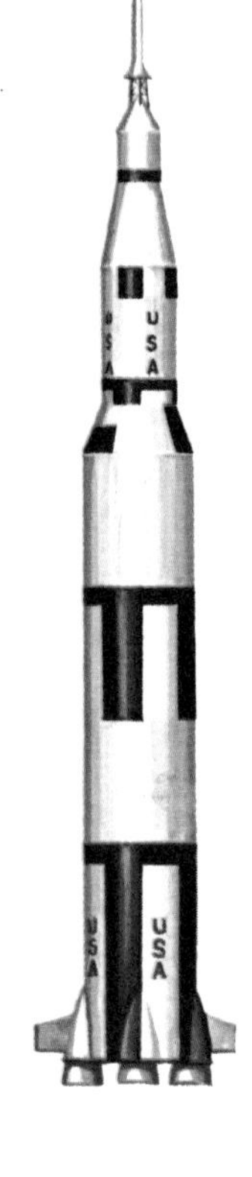

hammer

nail

rocket

toolbox

telephone

plants

Things

pick

shovel

building

guitar

banjo

spatula

candy

wax paper

a b c d e f g h i j k l m n
o p q r s t u v w x y z

alphabet

A B C D E F G H I J K L M
N O P Q R S T U V W X Y Z

alphabet

Places

airport

park

aquarium

zoo

city

Places

farm

field

country

Acknowledgments

The illustrations in this book are by:

Jack Wallen, pages 17-18, 45, 68
Justin Wager, pages 19-23
Bob Keys, pages 24-25, 77-78
Gene Rosner, page 26
Jerry Pinkney, pages 32-36, 101
Rainey Bennett, pages 38-44
The Graphic Group, pages 46-47, 82-83
Jack White, pages 48-55, 110-116
Tye Gibson, pages 61-67
Joe Rogers, pages 70-76
Marg. Moran, page 80 (middle)
Roy Anderson, pages 84-89
Lois Axeman, page 90
Rod Ruth, pages 92-97
Dick Scott, pages 98-100
George Suyeoka, pages 102-109

The photographs in this book are by:

James L. Ballard, cover, page 79
Paul Sequeira, pages 1, 7, 37, 69, 91
Wm. Franklin McMahon, pages 8-12, 16, 59, 81 (bottom right)
J. W. Moore, pages 13-15
The Chicago Tribune, pages 27-28
Chicago Zoological Society, pages 29-31
Bethlehem Steel Corporation, page 56
Julian Caraballo/ Tom Stack Associates, page 57
National Coal Association, page 58
New York Fire Department, page 60
U.S.D.A., National Peanut Research Laboratory, Dawson, Georgia,
page 80 (top and bottom), page 81 (top left and right, bottom left)

1 2 3 4 5 6 7 8 9 10 11 12 13 14 15 16 17 18 19 20 21 22 23 24 25 80 79 78 77 76 75 74 73